READING
SKILLS BOOK

LEVEL 8

Carnival time for Joshua

Answer in sentences.

1   What instrument did Joshua's dad play?

2   What were the team from Joshua's street dressing up as?

3   How did Joshua help to make the costumes?

4   What did Mum and Dad wear on the day of the carnival?

5   Look at the picture on pages 6 and 7. Choose two of the lorries and describe what the people are wearing and doing.

6   Why did Joshua run off into the crowd?

7   Do you think he should have done this? Why?

8   Why couldn't Granny tell where Joshua had gone?

9   How do you think Granny felt when Joshua ran off?

10   What would you do if you got lost?

Read the story. Try to answer the questions without looking back at the book. Answer in sentences.

1 How long do people celebrate the Chinese New Year for?

2 How do people get ready for the Chinese New Year festival?

3 What is one of the special things that people eat at Chinese New Year?

4 What do visitors take when they go to see their friends at Chinese New Year?

5 Which colour is said to be lucky for Chinese people?

6 Which animal should have won the swimming race?

7 Why can you only see people's legs under the dragon costume?

The stories in this book are about different festivals. Look through the book to find the answers to these questions. Answer in sentences.

1 Which festival is also known as the Festival of Light?

2 Which festival do the children in Mrs Dale's class celebrate?

3 Which festival are the children getting ready for in "The big tidy-up"?

4 There is one poem in this book. Which festival is it about?

5 Some people eat special sweets and dumplings and wish each other luck on this festival. Which festival is it?

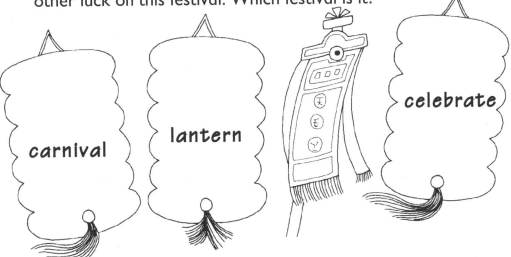

6 Look up the above words in a dictionary and explain what they mean in your own words.

Read the sentences. When did each of these things happen?
Read "Danny's diary" to find out. Write a sentence to say which day
it was.

1   I put the album back in the cupboard under the stairs.

2   The wind blew my ice-cream on to the picture an artist
was painting.

3   Mum came to take me home today.

4   I helped Aunt Daisy to tidy the cupboard under the stairs.

5   I have come to stay with Great Aunt Daisy.

6   The artist had painted a picture of Great Aunt Daisy.

7   I took the photograph album to the beach and some of the
pages blew away.

Danny's diary

Make up your own diary for a week. Write down one thing that happened each day.

Monday
I went to visit Sally. I played with her video game.

Tuesday
We did P.E. at school. I got the best score in rounders.

Wednesday
We went swimming today. I went to the library after school.

Thursday Went to play with John. Uncle Derek cooked spaghetti!

Friday

Saturday

Sunday

Answer in sentences.

1 Write a short message to a friend. Write your message in Morse code.

2 Make a list of the ways you could send a Morse code message which people could hear.

3 Work with a friend to find out all you can about Samuel Morse, the man who invented Morse code.

(a) First list some questions about him that you would like to find answers to.

(b) Now find some books which might have information about him, for example encyclopedias, history books and books about codes and secret messages. Write down the answers that you find to your questions.

Comprehension/Information

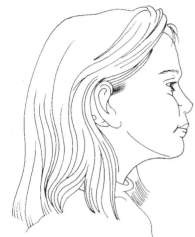

Answer in sentences.

1 What did Ella think about the new girl in the street when she first met her?

2 Why was Ella glad that a new girl had come to live in her street?

3 What did Ella's mum think made the new girl just stare and not speak when Ella spoke to her?

4 How could Michelle tell what people were saying?

5 What did Michelle's mum do when she came round for tea?

6 Why did Ella and her mum practise the finger spelling alphabet?

7 Think of three things that are difficult to do if you are deaf.

8 How do you think Michelle felt when she first started at Ella's school?

1. Look at the picture on page 32. Describe the girl who has moved into Anna's old flat. Say what she looks like and what she is wearing.

2. Read the story again. Make a list of all the words that describe what the girl looks like when she is a clown.

3. Pretend that you are the Mystery Girl. Write a letter that she might send to a friend.
    - Write about when she moved into her new flat.
    - Write about two things she does when she is a clown.
    - Write about what she likes best about being a clown.

Answer in sentences.

1 Why did Mum say Andrew couldn't have a picnic?

2 What was the little man like?

3 What had the little green man lost?

4 Whose friend was the Ice Queen?

5 Where did the little green man find his bag of springs?

6 What happened to the plants when the spring came?

Power from the wind

Read "Power from the wind" again. Try to answer the questions without looking back at the book. Answer in sentences.

1   What damage can hurricanes do?

2   What do the wheels do in a windmill?

3   What is a wind farm?

4   What is good about wind farms?

5   What happens when coal is used to make electricity?

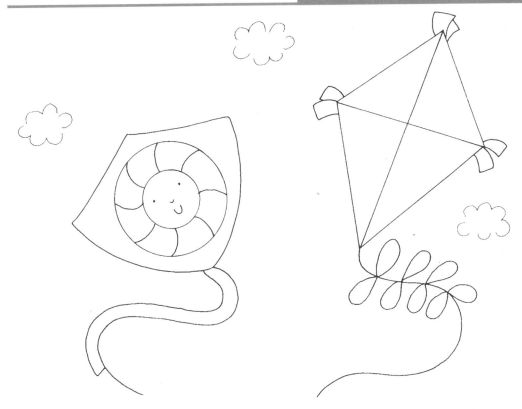

6   Write down three things that use the wind to move.

7   Why are wind farms often by the sea?

8   Where else in the countryside would be a good place for a wind farm?

9   Why can't people use hot air balloons to get to where they want to go?

10   Do you think all the electricity we need could be made using wind farms?

When we are writing, we use speech marks (" ") to show that people are talking.

" goes at the beginning of what people say.

" goes at the end.

Like this:

Amit said, "I've got a new kite, Dada."

The kite

Look at the pictures and write what Amit and Dada say in your exercise book. Put in the speech marks.

Answer in sentences.

Look at the contents page.

1   How many stories are there?

2   How many pages are there in the second story?

3   Which is the longest story?

4   In which story would you read about flying kites?

5   In which story would you read about the spring?

6   What can you read about on page 30?

7   In which stories can you find these words?

     (a) wind sails electricity farm coal

     (b) spring picnic plant stone flowers

     (c) kite competitions monster handkerchief proud

     (d) squirrel lunch sandwiches frosty peanut

     (e) seaside summer swallow hurt water

8   In which stories can you find these pictures?

Catch!

1   Make a list of the characters in the story. Choose two characters and write some notes about each one.

Use this example to help you.

Mum has short dark hair. She is wearing trousers, a striped shirt and a jacket. She wants to go shopping. She goes to town on the bus with Ben and Liz.

2   Where does the story take place? Draw a plan showing where the characters go.

3   What happens in the story? Write down four things that happen.

4   Pretend you are Ben. Write down how Ben would tell the story.

Great Grandma's birthday

Book 4: In our family

Answer in sentences.

1   Look at the pictures of Great Grandma on pages 22 and 23.
         Describe what she is wearing.

2   Pretend you are Great Grandma. Tell the story of your
         birthday party.

3   What year will it be if you live to be 100 years old?

4   Write about what you think you would like to do on your
         100th birthday.

5   Write about how you think the following things will have
         changed:
         (a) cars
         (b) school
         (c) clothes

Responding to reading

Read the story. Try to answer the questions without looking back at the book. Answer in sentences.

1   Why did everyone like to come and stay at Adam's house?

2   Who came to stay for three weeks?

3   How long did Auntie Jo stay in bed every day?

4   Why did Auntie Sophie come to stay?

5   What did Uncle Rob do when he saw Adam?

6   Why did Uncle Rupert change the wheel of his car?

7   Where did Auntie Kay take Adam?

8   What did Auntie Kay show Adam in the woods?

Comprehension

9 What might Adam not like about people coming to stay?

10 Why was Adam tired and hungry after seeing the sunrise?

11 What sort of person do you think Auntie Kay is?

12 Do you think Adam's mother likes everyone coming to stay?

Answer in sentences. The words in the vase might help you.

surprised   worried   pleased

sad   unhappy   excited

cross   proud   happy

angry   silly

frightened

1 How did Jake feel when he had to look after Rosie?

2 How did Jake feel when he found Rosie had stopped the video recording a programme for Dad?

3 How did Jake's mum feel when she saw him mending her favourite ornament?

4 How did Adam feel when everyone told him to be quiet?

Responding to reading

5   How did Adam feel when Auntie Kay took him to the woods?

6   How do you think Adam felt when Auntie Kay left?

7   How did Great Grandma feel when it was her birthday?

8   How did Great Grandma feel when she went for her boat trip?

9   How did Ben feel when he kept dropping the frisbee?

10   How did Ben feel when the policeman thanked him for catching a thief?

The fox and the kitten

Read the story. Try to answer the questions without looking back at the book. Answer in sentences.

1   What did Mrs Fox think she would find to eat at the farm?

2   What did Mrs Fox see as she ran past the farmhouse?

3   Where did the kitten take Mrs Fox?

4   What did the kitten say Mrs Fox would see if she looked down the well?

5   What did Mrs Fox really see down the well?

6   What did the kitten say was kept down the well?

7   What happened when the kitten jumped in the top bucket?

8   What happened to the kitten when Mrs Fox jumped into the second bucket?

9   Why did Mrs Fox hunt for food at night?

10   What would have happened if Mrs Fox hadn't jumped into the second bucket?

1   Do you think the kitten knew what would happen when Mrs Fox got into the second bucket?

2   Think of some things that cats and foxes have in common.

Exclamation marks look like this: **!**

They are used after words that are said loudly or suddenly. Like this:

> "Stop, thief!" shouted the policeman.

Look at the pictures and write what the people say in your exercise book. Put in the speech marks and exclamation marks.

Make up some sentences that use the following words in what people say. Put in the speech marks and exclamation marks.

1	look out	**6**	shut the door
2	hurry up	**7**	let me go
3	get out	**8**	go to bed
4	stop that noise	**9**	well done
5	don't shout	**10**	be quick

The mice who saved the moon

shared shadow

roar den howl

1   List the above words in alphabetical order. Look up the words in a dictionary and write down what each one means.

2   The words below have more than one meaning. Look them up in a dictionary and write down two meanings for each word.

down

bat

worry

Write a sentence for each meaning.

Answer in sentences.

1   Who are the main characters in the story? Write a sentence for each one, saying what job they do.

2   What is this story about? What was the strange thing that kept happening?

3   What strange things spoke to the characters? Write down one thing that each of them said.

4   Pretend you write stories for a newspaper. Write a newspaper article about what happened. Say whether you think the story is true.

5   What would something of yours say if it could talk?

Read the story. Try to answer the questions without looking back at the book. Answer in sentences.

1 What sort of person was Hamood?

2 What sort of person was Hameed?

3 Where did Hamood and Hameed live?

4 What happened when Hamood started to polish the lamp that he had found?

5 What was Hamood's third wish?

6 Why did the villagers like Hamood so much?

7 What difference would it make to the villagers to live in an oasis?

8 What might have happened if Hameed had found the lamp?

9 Which do you think was Hamood's best wish? Why?

10 What do you think Hameed could have done to try to be happy?

Answer the questions in sentences. The words in the box might help you.

happy   pleased   unhappy   frightened   proud   surprised excited   worried   lonely   sad   silly   angry

1   How did the farmer feel when the pumpkin spoke to him?

2   How did Hamood feel when the genie gave him three wishes?

3   How did Miss Pearson feel when the giant put his foot in the school playground?

4   How did the people who lived near the sea monster feel?

5   How did Peter the parrot feel when everyone had gone and the castle was locked up?